# This Book Belongs To

_____

ISBN: 978-1-950649-67-9

Illustrations : Kimmel Hayward

Cover Design: Life Chronicles Publishing

Life Chronicles Publishing Copyright © 2021

lifechroniclespublishing.com

# Daddy Don't Go

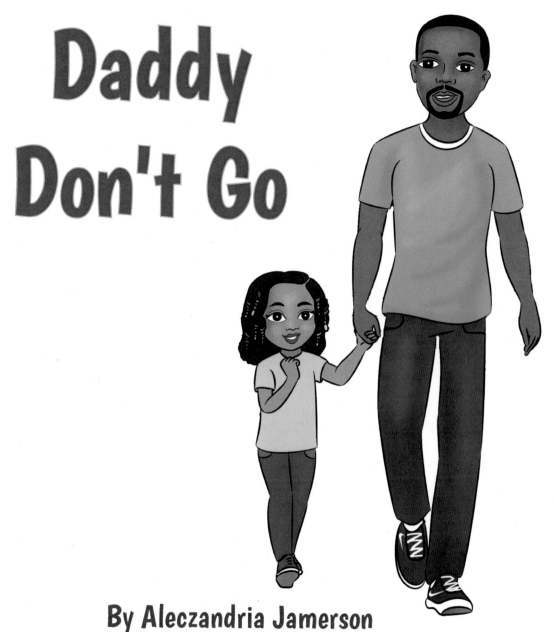

By Aleczandria Jamerson

Illustrated by Kimmel Hayward

Days go by and nights go too. I count them down until I see YOU. And when I do, my face lights up. I yell and cheer, "I am so happy to have YOU here!"

When my Daddy sleeps, I hear him snore. It's deep and loud like a lion's roar, but I don't tremble, and I don't wake. I love the sleeping sounds my Daddy makes.

He is so silly; he is so fun. He plays his old school jams, and he sings along. He closes his eyes, and he snaps his fingers. My Daddy even hits the notes and has moves just like the singers!

My Daddy is a chef too. My favorite dish is his Fettuccini. I love my Daddy's cooking sooo much, even more than his singing. I almost forgot I love his gumbo too! I don't think there is anything my Daddy can't do!!

He tells me I'm special; he tells me I'm sweet.
He buys me comfy socks and cool shoes for my feet.
And when I act up, like don't do
my homework or listen.

My Daddy gets stern, and he says it's because he has to teach me things I should learn.

"Stay away from boys." He says. My Daddy is so silly. "Be respectful, well mannered, honest, and not too friendly." I listen and laugh as he continues. "These are jewels I'm giving you, tools you will use, and don't take them for granted. It is my job to water you. You're like the seeds we planted."

He tells me he loves me all the time, as if he thinks I cannot tell. Even when I go to time out, I know my Daddy means well. He protects and provides for me and my brother, and he says we are the greatest gifts sent to him through my Mother.

My Daddy isn't like other Dads, which makes him unique. When everyone else is lying down, we watch movies until we sleep. My Daddy is my teddy bear, and he can fill the room with his laughter. And sometimes, when we stay up late, we pay for it the morning after.

As the days go on, I wish we could spend time with each other forever, but Daddy has to go off to work, so we have less time to spend together. That makes me angry, and it makes me mad, and then I even start to cry because I feel sad.

I begin to think of an idea (ah-ha) I found it!
Here Daddy, here is my piggy bank. I think
I have enough for all the bills, count it!!

I looked into his eyes; he was looking at me. His eyes had tears; that's all I could see. He said, "Baby, one day you will understand." Then we walk to the driveway holding hands.

Until my Daddy comes home again. I think of our fun days, which helps me feel better whenever he's away. Some trips are long; sometimes they're short, and sometimes we just don't know. But I'm getting better at saying, "see you later." When it's his time to roll.

I have my Mom, my Aunties, my Uncles, good Friends, and I have my brother too. My Abuelita, my Papa Deuces, and my cousins, to name a Few.

So, when I'm Feeling sad and miss my Daddy coming home. I love on those that hold me close when Daddy has to go.

# The End